THE
PRIMARY
MATHEMATICS
HANDBOOK

SPACE ■ MEASUREMENT ■ NUMBER

DICTIONARY OF MATHEMATICAL TERMS

HARRY O'BRIEN
GREG PURCELL

HORWITZ
MARTIN

Foreword

The Primary Mathematics Handbook is a reference book for primary school students, their parents and teachers. It is a valuable resource which will assist understanding of the concepts being developed in contemporary mathematics syllabus documents.

The book has four distinct sections, namely, **Number**, **Space**, **Measurement**, and a **Dictionary of Mathematical Terms**. The Dictionary is cross-referenced to the three major strands of Space, Measurement and Number.

Concise definitions, using simple language and appropriate examples, are employed to assist the reader gain a clear understanding of mathematical processes. Diagrams are used extensively to support the definitions and to provide a clear impression of concepts. Charts of tables, addition facts, properties of shapes, Roman numerals, fractions, decimals and percentages provide ready access to information which can assist the reader to consolidate knowledge and solve problems.

The Dictionary defines the meanings of words as used in their mathematical context. Examples, diagrams and cross-references are provided to aid in the understanding of these terms.

HORWITZ
MARTIN

Published by:
Horwitz Publications Pty Ltd.
55 Chandos Street, St Leonards NSW 2065 Australia

Prim-Ed Distributed in the United Kingdom and Ireland by Prim-Ed Publishing.

9003

EDITOR: Beverley Weynton
COVER DESIGN: Richard Tabaka
ILLUSTRATIONS: Jane Wade
GRAPHICS: Richard Tabaka
COMPUTER PAGE COMPOSITION: ID Studio, Sydney

Printed in Australia by Sands Group, WA.

98 99 00
1 2 3 4

Contents

SIGNS AND TERMINOLOGY

+	add, addition, plus		( )	parentheses
−	minus, subtraction, take away		{ }	braces
×	multiply, multiplication		[ ]	brackets
÷	divide, division; other symbols for division are)__ and)⎺		°	degree
			∠	angle
=	equals, equal to		△	triangle
≠	is not equal to		□	square
<	less than		▭	rectangle
>	greater than		○	circle
≤	is less than or equal to		▱	parallelogram
≥	is greater than or equal to		⌒	arc
≮	not less than		↔	line
≯	not greater than		↦	ray
∞	infinity		•—•	interval
%	percent, percentage		‖	parallel
.	decimal point		π	pi 3.14

SI   Systeme   Internationale

length

m	metre – the basic unit of length
cm	centimetre
dm	decimetre
mm	millimetre
km	kilometre

area

m^2	square metre
cm^2	square centimetre
mm^2	square millimetre
ha	hectare
km^2	square kilometre

volume

l	litre
ml	millilitre
cm^3	cubic centimetre
m^3	cubic metre

mass

kg	kilogram – the basic SI unit for mass
g	gram
t	tonne

time

d	day
h	hour
min	minute
s	second
a.m.	ante meridiem (before noon)
p.m.	post meridiem (after noon)
B.C.	before Christ
A.D.	in the year of our Lord (Anno Domini)

temperature

°C	degree Celsius

rates

km/h	kilometres per hour
G.M.T.	Greenwich Mean Time

Number

NUMERATION

The Reading of Numbers

The place value of a numeral is indicated by where it is in the number. Therefore **6** in the number **6 207** represents **six thousand**.

When we read numbers, we read them in groups of hundreds, tens and ones.

The following chart best illustrates this concept.

Examples

		MILLIONS			THOUSANDS			ONES		
		Hund's	Tens	Ones	Hund's	Tens	Ones	Hund's	Tens	Ones
1.	206 341				2	0	6	3	4	1
2.	257 403 280	2	5	7	4	0	3	2	8	0

H T O   H T O
Example 1   reads **2 0 6** thousand **3 4 1** ones

H T O   H T O   H T O
Example 2   reads **2 5 7** million **4 0 3** thousand **2 8 0** ones

Note   We no longer use commas to separate place value because in some countries the comma has the equivalent meaning of a decimal point. A space now separates place value groups of millions, thousands and ones.

Number Symbols

Different cultures have different number notations. Some of them are:

HINDU-ARABIC	ROMAN	JAPANESE	HINDU-ARABIC	ROMAN	JAPANESE
1	I	一	9	IX	九
2	II	二	10	X	十
3	III	三	20	XX	二十
4	IV	四	30	XXX	三十
5	V	五	50	L	五十
6	VI	六	100	C	百
7	VII	七	500	D	五百
8	VIII	八	1000	M	千

Some numbers have been given particular names.

Prime Numbers

A counting number which has no factors other than itself and one.

Examples

2	3	5	7	11	13	17	19	23	29
31	37	41	43	47	53	59	61	67	71
73	79	83	89	97	131	267			

Composite Numbers

A number which is the product of two numbers other than itself and 1.

Examples of composite numbers and some of their factors.

$4 = 2 \times 2$ $6 = 3 \times 2$ $8 = 4 \times 2$ $9 = 3 \times 3$ $10 = 5 \times 2$

$12 = 6 \times 2$ $14 = 7 \times 2$ $15 = 5 \times 3$ $16 = 8 \times 2$ $18 = 9 \times 2$

$12 = 3 \times 4$ $16 = 4 \times 4$ $18 = 6 \times 3$

Ordinal Numbers

An ordinal number is used to indicate position.

Examples   1st = first   3rd = third   5th = fifth

Odd Numbers

Odd numbers are not divisible by 2.

Examples   1   3   5   7   9   11   13   15   17   19

Even Numbers

Even numbers are divisible by 2.

Examples   2   4   6   8   10   12   14   16   18   20

Cardinal Numbers

The number of objects in a group.

Example   Cardinal number = 3

Whole Numbers

Whole numbers are the counting numbers.

Examples   0*   1   2   3   4   5   6   7

 * Zero is a place holder

Rational Numbers

The set of rational numbers includes positive and negative numbers, zero, fractions and decimal fractions.

Examples   -14   -8   -1   0 $\frac{3}{10}$ $\frac{5}{8}$ .75   6

Addition Algorithm using Regrouping

Regrouping is based on the facts that
- 10 ones equal 1 ten
- 10 tens equal 1 hundred
- 10 hundreds equal 1 thousand

Example   **268 + 49**

STEP 1	
• 8 and 9 is 17 • 17 is comprised of 1 ten and 7 ones • 7 is placed on the answer line in the ones column • 1 ten is carried to the tens place	H T U 2 6 8 + 4 9 ——— 7 1

STEP 2	
• 1 ten is added to the 4 tens • That is 5 tens so far • 5 tens is added to the 6 tens • There are 11 tens • 11 tens is comprised of 1 hundred and 1 ten • 1 is placed on the answer line in the tens place • 1 hundred is carried to the hundreds place	H T U 2 6 8 + 4 9 ——— 1 7 1 1

STEP 3	
• 1 hundred is added to the 2 hundreds • That is 3 hundreds • 3 is placed on the answer line in the hundreds place	H T U 2 6 8 + 4 9 ——— 3 1 7 1 1

Examples

1.　6 8 5 8
　　+ 6 2 7
　　7 4 8 5
　　1　 1

2.　3 5 7 9
　　+ 3 9 2
　　3 9 7 1
　　　1 1

3.　2 5 8 8
　　+1 5 0 9
　　4 0 9 7
　　1　 1

SUBTRACTION METHODS

Take Away

A specified number of objects is taken away from a larger group. Children describe what has happened.

Example   **8 take away 2 leaves 6**

Comparing

Comparing is seeing what the difference is.

There are two more black cats than white cats.
The difference is 2.
There are two fewer white cats than black cats.

Counting On

Counting on involves matching one group with another and counting the remainder in the larger group.

Number Line

Count back the appropriate number of places to determine how many are left.

Example   **14 − 6 = 8**

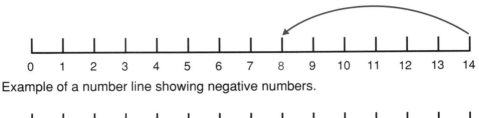

Example of a number line showing negative numbers.

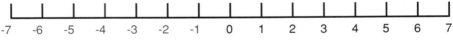

Subtraction Algorithm

The subtraction algorithm is the symbolic representation of subtraction.

Example

$$
\begin{array}{r}
7 \\
-\ 3 \\
\hline
4
\end{array}
$$

7 ————— minuend
− 3 ————— subtrahend
4 ————— difference

Base 10 Materials

Base 10 materials can be used to represent a subtraction problem.

Example   **38 − 16 = ☐**

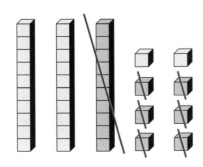

16 have been taken away, leaving 22

Regrouping

Regrouping is based on the fact that one ten is comprised of ten ones.

Example 1   26 – 9 = ☐

One ten is exchanged so that 26 now looks like this.

9 ones are taken away from the group of one ten and sixteen ones to show 17 remaining.

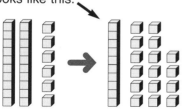

26 – 9 = 17

Example 2   923 – 608 = ☐

"To take 8 ones from 3 ones I exchanged two tens for one ten and ten ones. That gave me nine hundreds, one ten and thirteen ones."

"Then I took away 8 ones and 6 hundreds, leaving 315."

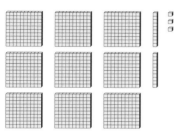

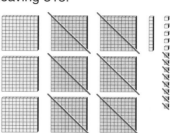

Decomposition

Example   9 3 4
              – 2 5 8

STEP 1	

• 8 from 4, can't do
• Regroup the 3 tens by regrouping so that there are 2 tens left in the tens column and 10 ones have been added to the original 4 to give 14 ones
• 8 ones are subtracted from 14 ones
• 6 is placed on the answer line in the ones place
	H T U
	
	  2 14
	9 3̶ 4
	– 2 5 8
	      6

STEP 2	
• 5 tens can't be subtracted from 2 tens • Regroup the 9 hundreds by regrouping so that there are 8 hundreds in the hundreds column and the 10 tens have been added to the 2 tens to give 12 tens in the tens column • 5 tens are subtracted from 12 tens • 7 is placed on the answer line in the tens place	H T U 8 12 14 9̶ 3̶ 4 – 2 5 8 7 6
STEP 3	
• Subtract 2 hundreds from the 8 hundreds • 6 is placed on the answer line in the hundreds place	H T U 8 12 14 9̶ 3̶ 4 – 2 5 8 6 7 6
(Examples on next page)	

Examples

1.	2.	3.	4.
6 14	7 14	1 14 11 16	8 9 9 10
7̶ 4	8̶ 4̶ 5	2̶ 5̶ 2̶ 6	9̶ 0̶ 0̶ 0
– 3 8	– 2 9 3	– 6 5 9	– 4 1 2 5
3 6	5 5 2	1 8 6 7	4 8 7 5

Subtraction can be checked by addition.

1.	2.	3.	4.
3 6	5 5 2	1 8 6 7	4 8 7 5
+ 3 8	+ 2 9 3	+ 6 5 9	+ 4 1 2 5
7 4	8 4 5	2 5 2 6	9 0 0 0

Shopkeeper's Method

The shopkeeper's method is based on the "counting on" method.

Example   **What change would I get if I bought 2 pens for 65p and I gave one pound?**

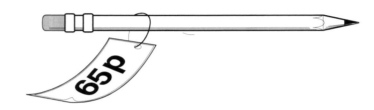

Pens 65p + (5) = 70p + (10) = 80p + (20) = £1.00

I received 35p change.

Equal Addends

This method is rarely used today.

Example

7 5 ⟶ 8 from 5, can't do. Add 10 to the 5 and add ⟶ 7¹5
– 3 8   10 to the subtrahend (38). This means both   –¹3 8
numbers have had their value increased by
10 as a convenient way of performing the
subtraction operation.

This is, 75 has been changed to 70 + 15.
38 has been changed to 40 + 8.

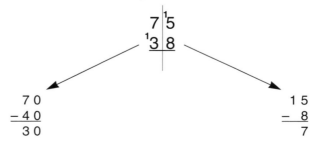

7 0	1 5
– 4 0	– 8
3 0	7

MULTIPLICATION METHODS

Multiplication is repeated addition, i.e. $5 \times 3 = 3 + 3 + 3 + 3 + 3 = 15$
Number facts, i.e. tables 1 to 12 are sometimes taught as related groups:
($\times 2$, $\times 4$) ($\times 10$, $\times 5$, $\times 1$, $\times 0$) ($\times 3$, $\times 6$) ($\times 8$) ($\times 7$)

Multiplication by 1 digit

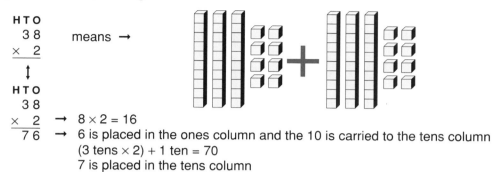

```
H T O
  3 8    means →
× 2
  ↕
H T O
  3 8
×   2   →  8 × 2 = 16
  7 6   →  6 is placed in the ones column and the 10 is carried to the tens column
           (3 tens × 2) + 1 ten = 70
           7 is placed in the tens column
```

Multiplication by 2 digits (Extended form)

Example

```
    6 4
  × 2 9   →   This is treated as (64 × 9) + (64 × 20)
                        3
                       6 4          6 4
                     ×   9        × 2 0
                       5 7 6   +   1 2 8 0   = 1 8 5 6
```

Contracted Form

Example   **STEPS**

```
      3
    6 4
  × 2 9
    5 7 6
  1 2 8 0
  1 8 5 6
```

- $9 \times 4 = 36$. Place 6 in the ones column
- Trade 3 into the tens column
- 9×6 tens = 54 tens + 3 tens = 57 tens
- Place 57 alongside the 6 ones
- Recognise '2' as 2 tens
  Therefore, 0 (zero) is placed in the units column on the second answer line
- Multiply $64 \times 2 = 128$
- 1280 is placed on the second answer line
- Add
```
      5 7 6
  + 1 2 8 0
    1 8 5 6
```

Estimation

When multiplying, children are expected to make reasonable estimates of the answer before calculating it.
The process of estimation uses basic multiplication facts as the launching pad.

Examples

- $3 \times 4 = 12$, therefore $3 \times 40 = 120$ and $3 \times 400 = 1200$
- $2 \times 98 = 200$ approximately, therefore $2 \times 980 = 2000$ approximately
- 29×64 is approximately equal to 30×60, using the knowledge that $3 \times 6 = 18$, the estimated answer should be 1 800

DIVISION METHODS

There are two forms of division: • sharing   • grouping

Sharing

Example   **If nine toys are shared among three children, how many does each person get?**

Grouping

Example   **How many groups of 3 can be made from a bunch of 12 flowers?**

Repeated Subtraction

Repeated subtraction is a form of grouping

Example   **34 ÷ 8**   ➔

```
      4 r 2
  8 ) 3 4
  −   8
     2 6
  −   8
     1 8
  −   8
     1 0
  −   8
        2
```

Four groups of 8 can be subtracted from 34 with a remainder of 2

The Division Algorithm

Example   **Share 98 between 6 people**

```
      1 6 r 2
  6 ) 9 8
  −  6
     3 8
  − 3 6
        2
```

➔ • The 9 tens are shared, each person receives 1 ten

➔ • The remaining 3 tens are regrouped to ones
   • There are now 38 ones to share with each person receiving 6

➔ • This uses 36 ones with a remainder of 2

Symbolic Form

Example **6) 7 5 6** ➔ • 6 into 7 hundreds goes once, remainder 1

```
      1
  6 ) 7 5 6
```
➔ • Place 1 on the answer line in the hundreds place

```
      1 2
  6 ) 7¹5 6
```
➔ • Regroup the remaining hundred into 10 tens, therefore creating 15 tens

```
      1 2
  6 ) 7¹5 6
```
➔ • 6 into 15 tens goes 2 times with 3 remaining
   Place 2 on the answer line in the tens place

```
      1 2
  6 ) 7¹5³6
```
➔ • Exchange the remaining 3 tens for 30 ones, therefore creating 36 ones

```
      1 2 6
  6 ) 7¹5³6
```
➔ • 6 into 36 goes 6 times. Place 6 on the answer line in the ones place

Estimation

When dividing, we are expected to make estimations to determine the reasonableness of an answer.

Knowledge of tables and place value combined with the ability to round off assist when estimating.

Example   **158 ÷ 8 =** ☐

By rounding off 158 to the nearest ten, i.e. 160, and recalling the table fact that 16 = 8 × 2, it is reasonable to estimate the answer to be about 2 tens, i.e. 20.

158 → 160

16 ÷ 8 = 2, therefore 160 ÷ 8 = 20

FRACTIONS, DECIMALS AND PERCENTAGES
(Rational Number)

Fractions, decimals and percentages are different ways of expressing the same idea.

Fractions

A fraction is part of a whole. The fraction 3/5 represents 3 parts out of 5. The top part of each fraction is called the **numerator** and the bottom part is called the **denominator**. Hundredths and tenths are important fractions because of their ready use with decimals and percentages.

Examples

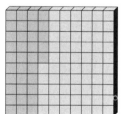

35 hundredths

$= \frac{35}{100}$

$= 0.35$

$= 35\%$

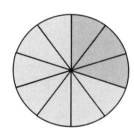

3 tenths

$= \frac{3}{10}$ or $\frac{30}{100}$

$= 0.3$

$= 30\%$

Decimals

A decimal is a numeral where the decimal point is used to separate the fractional part of the number from the whole number. A zero is used to hold the place where there is no whole number or where a required number of decimal places is required.

Examples $^{23}/_{100} = 0.23$ $^{1}/_{100} = 0.01$ $^{1}/_{10} = 0.1$

$^{1}/_{5} = 0.2$ $4^{1}/_{10} = 4.1$ $4^{7}/_{100} = 4.07$

Decimal Place Value

Example   2 2 2 2 2 . 2 2 2

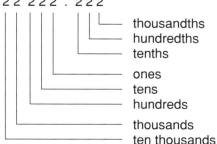

thousandths
hundredths
tenths

ones
tens
hundreds

thousands
ten thousands

Percentages

A percentage is a fraction whose denominator is 100. A percentage sign **(%)** is used to display percentages.

Example: A score of **85 out of 100** in a test can be viewed as **85%**.

Fractions, Decimals and Percentages

Fraction	Visual Hundredth	Decimal	Percentage
$^1/_{100}$		0.01	1%
$^1/_{10}$		0.1	10%
$^2/_{10}$ or $^1/_5$		0.2	20%
$^3/_{10}$		0.3	30%
$^4/_{10}$ or $^2/_5$		0.4	40%

Fraction	Visual Hundredth	Decimal	Percentage
$^5/_{10}$ or $^1/_2$		0.5	50%
$^6/_{10}$ or $^3/_5$		0.6	60%
$^7/_{10}$		0.7	70%
$^8/_{10}$ or $^4/_5$		0.8	80%
$^9/_{10}$		0.9	90%
1		1.0	100%

Fraction	Visual Hundredth	Decimal	Percentage
½		0.5	50%
¼		0.25	25%
¾		0.75	75%
93/100		0.93	93%

⅛ and ⅓ are important fractions that are referred to as part of a group.

Example: **35 children out of a grade of 105 scored highly in an exam.**

35/105 = ⅓

Space

2D SHAPES

Two-dimensional shapes are shapes with only two dimensions such as length and width. They are sometimes referred to as *plane shapes* as they occupy a flat surface.

circle	square	rectangle/oblong
semi circle	rhombus	parallelogram
equilateral triangle	right angle triangle	isosceles triangle
scalene triangle	trapezium	diamond (rhombus)
pentagon	hexagon	heptagon
irregular pentagon	irregular hexagon	irregular heptagon
octagon	nonagon	decagon
irregular octagon	irregular nonagon	irregular decagon

THE CIRCLE

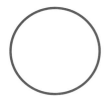

A circle is a shape bounded by a continuous curved line that is always the same distance from its centre point.

The circumference is the length of a circle's boundary or perimeter.

The diameter is a line that passes through the centre point of a circle to the circumference at each side.

The radius is a line reaching from the centre of the circle to its circumference.

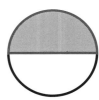

A semicircle is exactly half a circle.

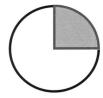

A quadrant is one quarter of a circle.

A chord is a line that joins two points on the circumference of a circle.

A sector is a shape bounded by two radii and the arc of a circle.

A segment is a shape bounded by a straight line and the arc of a circle.

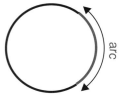

The arc is a part of the circumference of a circle bounded by two points.

TRIANGLES

A triangle is a three-sided shape with three angles. The total of the angles adds to 180°.

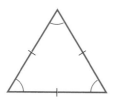

An **Equilateral Triangle** has three sides the same length and three angles the same size.

An **Isosceles Triangle** has two sides the same length and two angles the same size.

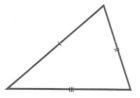

A **Scalene Triangle** has no sides the same length and no angles the same size.

A **Right Angle Triangle** is a triangle with one right angle.

POLYGONS

A polygon is any 2D shape that has 3 or more straight sides and angles.

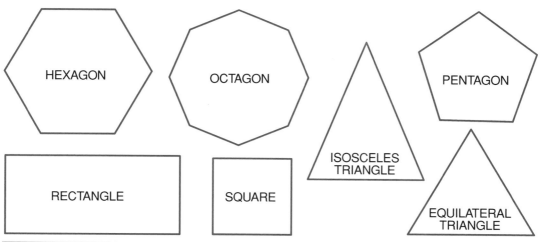

HEXAGON

OCTAGON

PENTAGON

ISOSCELES TRIANGLE

RECTANGLE

SQUARE

EQUILATERAL TRIANGLE

SHAPE	SIDES	NUMBER OF ANGLES	RIGHT ANGLES > = <	LINES OF SYMMETRY
Equilateral Triangle	3	3	<	3
Isosceles Triangle	3	3	<	1
Square	4	4	=	4
Rectangle	4	4	=	2
Pentagon	5	5	>	5
Hexagon	6	6	>	6
Octagon	8	8	>	8

QUADRILATERALS

A quadrilateral is any plane shape with four sides and four angles. The total of the angles adds up to 360°. The following are quadrilaterals.

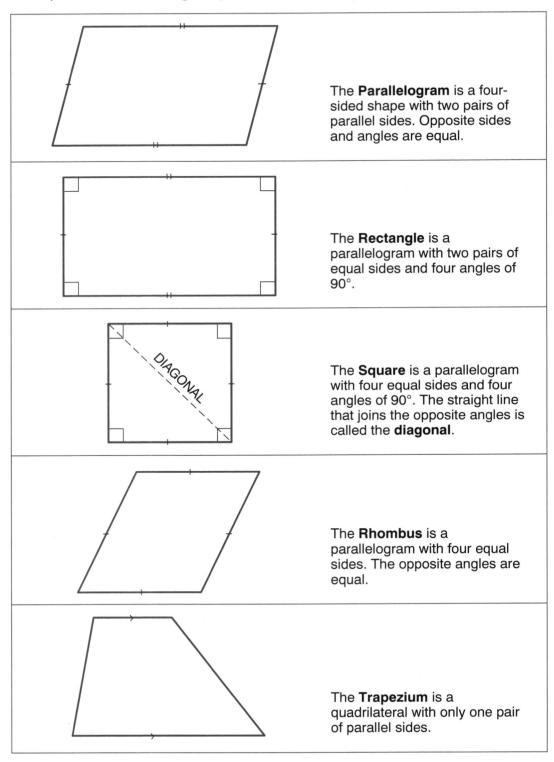

The **Parallelogram** is a four-sided shape with two pairs of parallel sides. Opposite sides and angles are equal.

The **Rectangle** is a parallelogram with two pairs of equal sides and four angles of 90°.

The **Square** is a parallelogram with four equal sides and four angles of 90°. The straight line that joins the opposite angles is called the **diagonal**.

The **Rhombus** is a parallelogram with four equal sides. The opposite angles are equal.

The **Trapezium** is a quadrilateral with only one pair of parallel sides.

LINES

————————————	Horizontal Line
	Vertical Line
	Parallel Lines
	Sloping Line (oblique line)
	Perpendicular Lines
	Curved Line
	Closed Curve

TESSELLATIONS

Shapes tessellate if they fit together in a geometric pattern. Bathroom tiles are excellent examples of tessellating shapes.

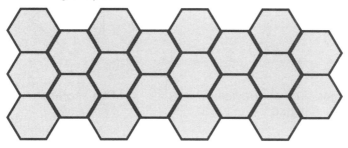

SYMMETRY

A shape is said to have symmetry if both its parts match exactly when folded.

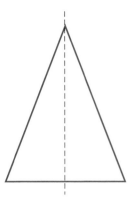

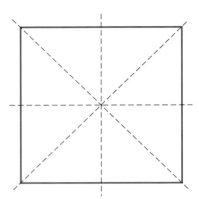

This triangle has only one line of symmetry.

A square has four lines of symmetry.

Reflective Symmetry

You can develop your skills in pattern-making by creating a mirror image of a shape.

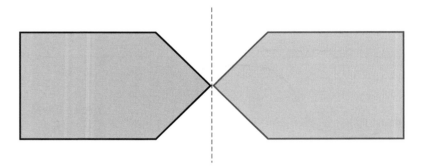

Rotational Symmetry

A shape has rotational symmetry if, after the shape is turned about a point, it matches the original shape.

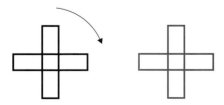

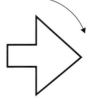

This shape turned 90° has rotational symmetry. It has matched the original.

This shape does not have rotational symmetry.

ANGLES

An **angle** is the amount of turning between two lines about a common point. The lines are called **rays** or **arms** and the common point is called the **vertex**.

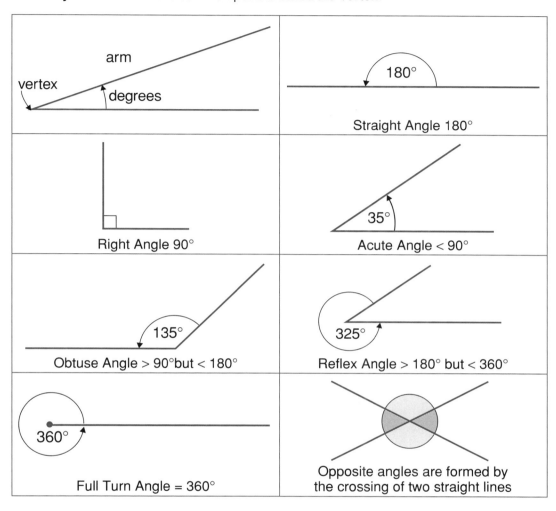

arm, vertex, degrees	180° — Straight Angle 180°
Right Angle 90°	35° — Acute Angle < 90°
135° — Obtuse Angle > 90° but < 180°	325° — Reflex Angle > 180° but < 360°
360° — Full Turn Angle = 360°	Opposite angles are formed by the crossing of two straight lines

Angle Facts

All **triangles** have 3 angles which total 180°.   All **quadrilaterals** have an angle total of 360°.

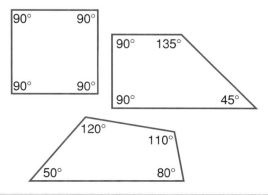

3D SHAPES

Three–dimensional shapes are solid shapes. They have three dimensions: length, width and height. 3D shapes are often classified according to the number of faces, edges and vertices each shape has.

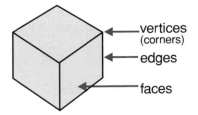

vertices (corners)

edges

faces

F = Faces   **E** = Edges   **V** = Vertices

Shape		Shape	
cube	**F** = 6 **E** = 12 **V** = 8	octagonal prism	**F** = 10 **E** = 24 **V** = 16
rectangular prism	**F** = 6 **E** = 12 **V** = 8	cylinder	**F** = 3 **E** = 2 **V** = 0
triangular prism	**F** = 5 **E** = 9 **V** = 6	sphere	**F** = 1 **E** = 0 **V** = 0
pentagonal prism	**F** = 7 **E** = 15 **V** = 10	hemisphere	**F** = 2 **E** = 1 **V** = 0
hexagonal prism	**F** = 8 **E** = 18 **V** = 12	cone	**F** = 2 **E** = 1 **V** = 1

square pyramid	F = 5 E = 8 V = 5	octagonal pyramid	F = 9 E = 16 V = 9
triangular pyramid (tetrahedron)	F = 4 E = 6 V = 4	hexahedron	F = 6 E = 9 V = 5
pentagonal pyramid	F = 6 E = 10 V = 6	octahedron	F = 8 E = 12 V = 6
icosahedron	F = 20 E = 30 V = 12	decahedron	F = 10 E = 20 V = 12
hexagonal pyramid	F = 7 E = 12 V = 7	dodecahedron	F = 12 E = 30 V = 20

NETS OF PRISMS

Nets are flat shapes which can be folded to form a three-dimensional shape. Here are some examples.

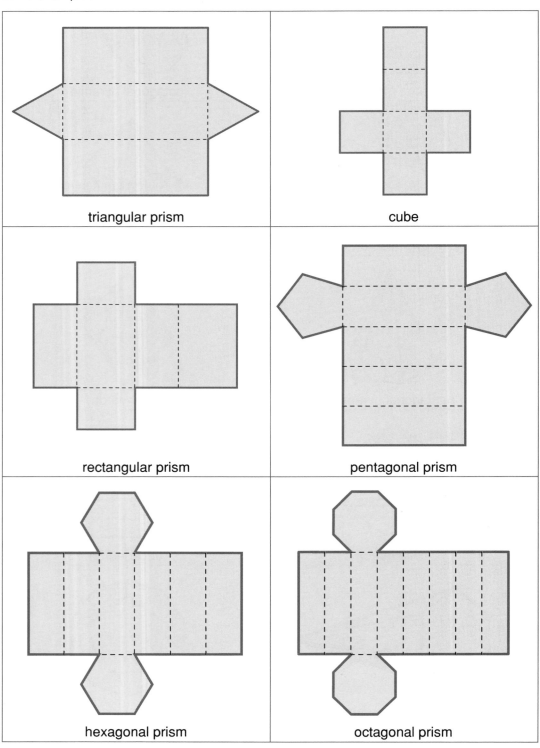

triangular prism	cube
rectangular prism	pentagonal prism
hexagonal prism	octagonal prism

NETS OF PYRAMIDS, CONE AND CYLINDER

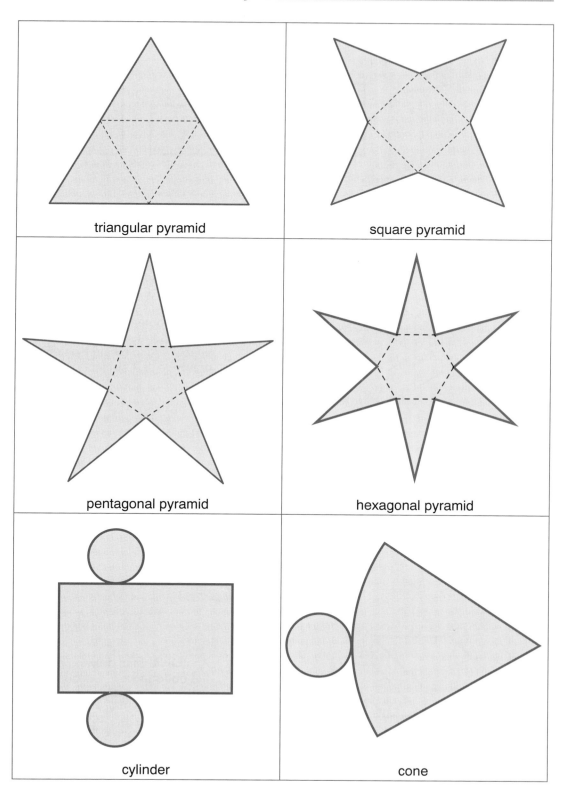

triangular pyramid

square pyramid

pentagonal pyramid

hexagonal pyramid

cylinder

cone

3D VIEWS, MODELLING AND PERSPECTIVE

3D Views

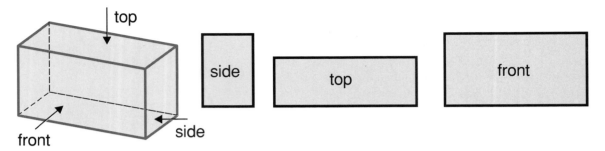

A 3D shape can be identified using its three views: top, front and side.

Modelling

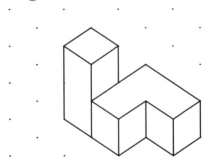

Models of 3D shapes can be constructed from isometric drawings. Isometric drawings use 3 axes. One is drawn vertically and the other two are at 30°. Isometric dot paper is marked with dots that reflect the axes and enable you to create isometric drawings of 3D objects.

Perspective

Perspective can be used when drawing 3D shapes.

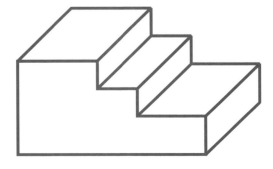

Another form of drawing perspective is the **oblique** view. Oblique drawings usually have the longest face drawn facing the observer. The other faces are drawn at an angle of 45° with the dimensions on that angle halved.

CHARTS AND GRAPHS

Charts and graphs are a useful means of representing data (gathered information). There are a number of graph types with specific purposes.

Bar charts

Bar charts can be vertical or horizontal and are used widely. They are very useful when recording results during simple probability activities.

Pictograms

Pictograms use a pictorial symbol to represent quantities. Four hundred and fifty children can be represented by

Line graphs

Line graphs should be used when meaning can be attached to the points on the line between the plotted points.

Pie charts

Pie charts are used to show how a total is divided.

Example

A probability experiment has been carried out on the tossing of a die thirty times. The following data was tallied using common tally marks. ⊞

| ⚀ III = 3 | ⚁ ⊞ = 5 | ⚂ IIII = 4 |
| ⚃ ⊞ I = 6 | ⚄ ⊞ = 5 | ⚅ ⊞ II = 7 |

From this information a bar chart was constructed to visually record the data.

The vertical axis is labelled with the numbers of occurrences of each number. (frequency)

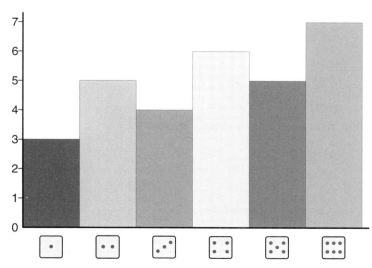

The horizontal axis is labelled with the numbers on the die faces.

CHANCE AND DATA

Language of Charts and Graphs

Probability
The numerical value of the chance of occurrence. For example, the probability of throwing and rolling a 6 on the die face is one chance in six.

Statistics
When graphing, statistics is the collection, organisation and presentation of data.

Data
Information gathered from which other facts or statements can be deduced.
(The information gathered for graphing.)

Frequency
In a collection of data, the frequency of a category is the number of occurrences for that category. For example, the frequency for the die face 1 in the chart on the previous page is 3.

Mean (average)
The arithmetic mean is a method for locating the centre of distribution. It is found by finding the total number of frequency responses and dividing it by the set of numbers or items that have been graphed. For example, the mean for the chart on the previous page is 30 frequency responses divided by six die faces. Therefore the mean equals 5.

Mode
The mode is the graphed number or item with the maximum frequency. For example, the number 6 in the chart on the previous page is its mode.

Median
The median is the graphed value with as many responses below it as above it. For example, the median for the chart on the previous page is 4 because it has 12 responses for the numbers 5 and 6 above it and 12 responses for the numbers 1, 2 and 3 below it.

Range
The range is the spread of distribution of scores. It ranges from the lowest frequency to the highest frequency. For example, the range for the chart on the previous page is 3 to 7.

Distribution
The whole set of recorded values for each number. The tallied information above the chart on the previous page is a grouped frequency distribution.

GRAPHS

Keys (Isotypes)
Keys are often used to define data in pictograms.

Example

= 10   **Therefore:**   = 30

Pictogram

Pets of our class

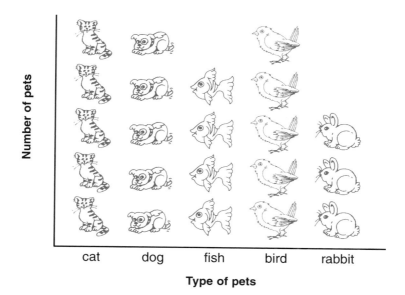

Bar Charts

Our group's maths marks

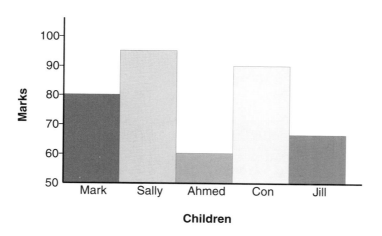

Favourite foods of *class 5L*

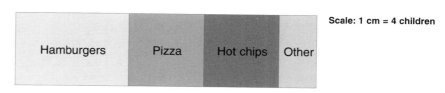

Scale: 1 cm = 4 children

32 children surveyed

Therefore:

Hamburgers = 12   Pizza = 8   Hot chips = 8   Other = 4

Line Graph

This week's temperatures

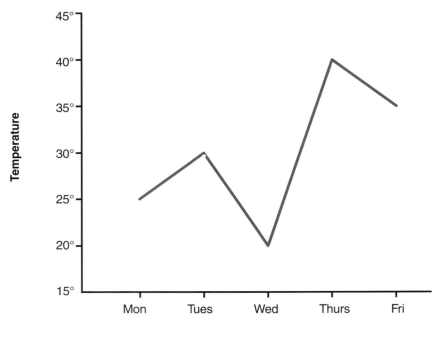

Days of the week

Pie Chart

Weekend boys' sport

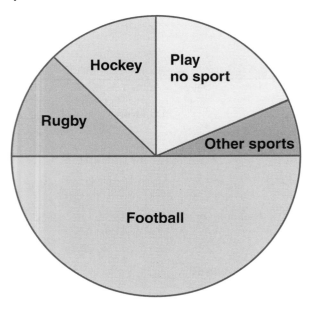

POSITION

The relationship between objects can be expressed in terms of position. This is done in the early years by using language to describe where objects are in relationship to themselves or another object. For example, the clock is to the right of the door.
Model-making or drawing sketches are also efficient ways of showing position.

Example: **My bedroom**

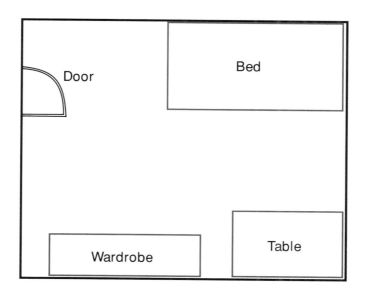

Following directions, giving simple directions or drawing paths on mazes and maps are further examples of position.

Example: **Maze**

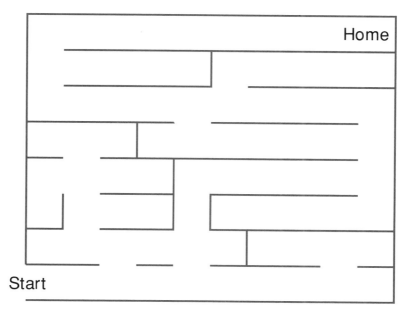

Measurement

PERIMETER

Perimeter is the distance around the outside of a shape.
Shapes with straight sides can be measured with a ruler or tape measure.
Longer distances can be measured with a trundle wheel.
The perimeter of curved surfaces can be measured with a piece of string which is placed around the boundary of the object. The string is then straightened and its length measured.

Examples

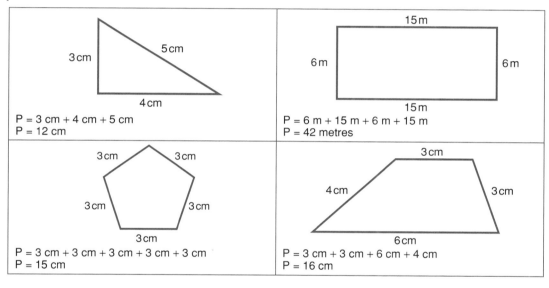

P = 3 cm + 4 cm + 5 cm
P = 12 cm

P = 6 m + 15 m + 6 m + 15 m
P = 42 metres

P = 3 cm + 3 cm + 3 cm + 3 cm + 3 cm
P = 15 cm

P = 3 cm + 3 cm + 6 cm + 4 cm
P = 16 cm

Circumference of a circle—using a calculator

A circle's perimeter is called its circumference. The formula for circumference is:

$$\boxed{C = 2\pi r}$$ i.e. Circumference = 2 × pi × radius of circle

You can use a calculator when finding the circumference of a circle.
- The radius of this circle is 2 cm.
- Pi (π) is approximately equal to 3.14

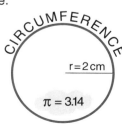

$C = 2\pi r$
$C = 2 \times 3.14 \times 2$ cm
$C = 6.28 \times 2$ cm
$C = 12.56$ cm

Pi

π= *circumference* ÷ diameter = 3.14 approximately
- If a piece of string is laid on top of the circle's perimeter it should measure 12.56 cm when straightened.

AREA

Area is the surface covered by any plane shape.
Initial investigation of area frequently involves comparison between two shapes.

Example

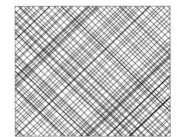

- The table cloth is larger than the tea towel.

- The tea towel is smaller than the table cloth.

- Six tea towels fit on the table cloth.

tea towel   table cloth

Informal units are used by younger children when measuring area.

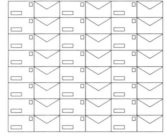

- I used 8 envelopes to cover the tea towel.

- I used 48 envelopes to cover the table cloth.

tea towel   table cloth

Area can be measured in square centimetres (cm^2), square metres (m^2), hectares (ha) and square kilometres (km^2).
The square, because its length and width are equal, provides the standard unit for measuring area.
The area of a rectangle is found by applying the formula:

Area = length $\times$ width

Examples

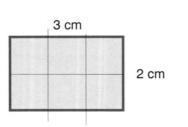

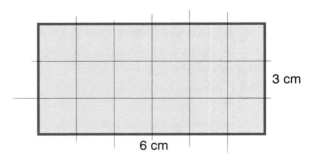

A = l $\times$ w
A = 3 cm $\times$ 2 cm
A = 6 cm^2

A = l $\times$ w
A = 6 cm $\times$ 3 cm
A = 18 cm^2

To calculate the area of other regions, break the region into appropriate shapes, e.g. rectangles.

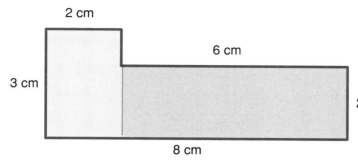

A = (3 × 2) + (6 × 2) cm²
A = 6 cm² + 12 cm²
A = 18 cm²

Area of a triangle—using a calculator

The area of a triangle is found by applying the formula:

| **A = 1/2 base × perpendicular height** |

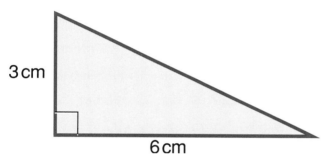

A = 1/2 b × ph
A = 1/2 (6 cm) × 3 cm
A = 3 cm × 3 cm
A = 9 cm²

This formula actually shows that a triangle is half the area of a rectangle of the same length and perpendicular height.

Area of a circle—using a calculator

The formula for the area of a circle is:

| **A = πr²** | i.e. Area = pi × radius × radius.

With the help of a calculator the area of a circle can be found.
- The radius of this circle is 2 cm.
- Pi (π) is approximately equal to 3.14.

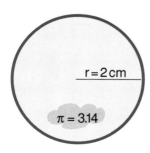

Area = π r²
A = 3.14 × (2 cm × 2 cm)
A = 3.14 × 4 cm²
A = 12.56 cm²

Hectares

One hectare (ha) is 10 000 m².

One hectare (ha) is 2.47 acres.

One acre is 4050 m² approximately.

Two football pitches are about 1 hectare.

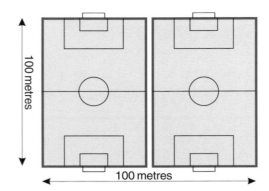

100 metres

100 metres

Square kilometres

Large areas such as continents and countries are measured in square kilometres.

One km² is 100 hectares.

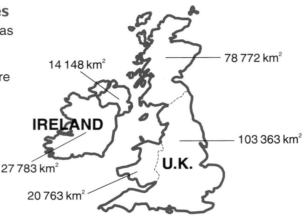

14 148 km²

78 772 km²

IRELAND

103 363 km²

27 783 km²

U.K.

20 763 km²

VOLUME AND CAPACITY

Volume is the amount of space an object occupies. **Capacity** is the amount a container can hold. Frequently, the terms *volume and capacity* are used interchangeably.

A brick has **volume** because it takes up space, it doesn't have **capacity**. A cup has **volume** because it takes up space and it also has **capacity** because it can hold a certain amount.

Arbitrary units are used by younger children when measuring volume and capacity.

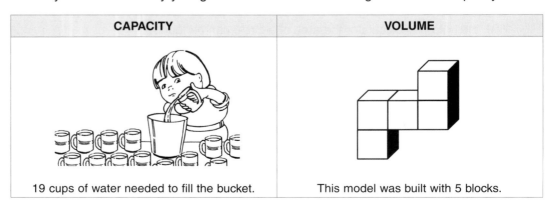

CAPACITY	VOLUME
19 cups of water needed to fill the bucket.	This model was built with 5 blocks.

The basic units for recording volume are the cubic metre (m³), cubic centimetre (cm³), litre (l) and millilitre (ml).

Volume of prisms and cubes

Volume = length × width × height

Example

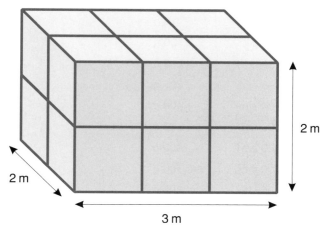

2 m

2 m

3 m

$V = l \times w \times h$
$V = 3\,m \times 2\,m \times 2\,m$
$V = 12\,m^3$

Other prisms

Volume = Area of base × height

Volume of cylinders—using a calculator

Volume = $\pi\,r^2 h$ i.e. Volume = pi × radius × radius × height

With the help of a calculator the volume of a cylinder can be found.
*   The radius of the base is 4 m.
*   The height is 5 m.
*   Pi (π) is approximately equal to 3.14.

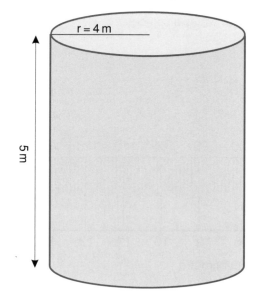

r = 4 m

5 m

$V = \pi \times r^2 \times h$
$V = 3.14 \times (4\,m \times 4\,m) \times 5\,m$
$V = 3.14 \times 16\,m^2 \times 5\,m$
$V = 50.24\,m^2 \times 5\,m$
$V = 251.2\,m^3$

Volume, capacity and mass are related

One millilitre of water has a mass of one gram and a volume of one cubic centimetre.

CAPACITY/WATER	VOLUME	MASS
1 ml	1 cm³	1 g
10 ml	10 cm³	10 g
100 ml	100 cm³	100 g
200 ml	200 cm³	200 g
300 ml	300 cm³	300 g
400 ml	400 cm³	400 g
500 ml	500 cm³	500 g
600 ml	600 cm³	600 g
700 ml	700 cm³	700 g
800 ml	800 cm³	800 g
900 ml	900 cm³	900 g
1 litre	1000 cm³	1 kilogram

Displacement

An object displaces its own volume when totally submerged in water.

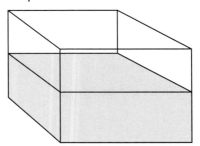 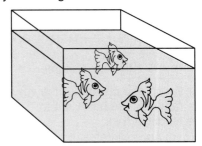

The volume of the fish is equal to the quantity of water displaced.
☆ **Volume is not the equivalent of mass.**

MEASUREMENT FACTS

Length

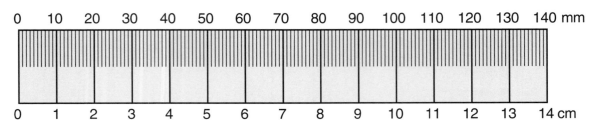

10 millimetres = 1 centimetre
100 centimetres = 1 metre
1000 metres = 1 kilometre

Using coordinates to describe position involves a formal grid where numbers or letters refer to the intersection of lines or spaces. Coordinate points are always read horizontally before vertically.

Example **The coordinate points (D,3) are circled.**

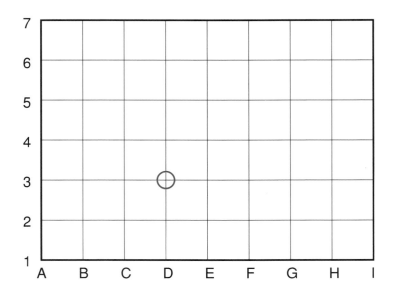

Working from compass points, using an atlas or a street directory and orienteering are all exercises at the primary level.

Example **Use compass points to describe the position of the palm tree in relation to the treasure.**

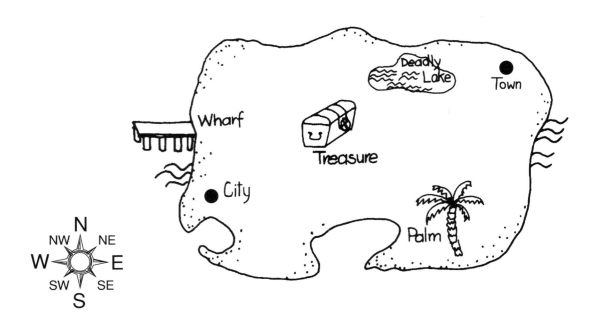

Area

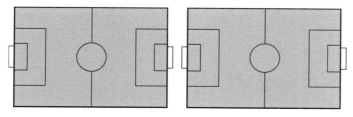

$$100 \text{ mm}^2 = 1 \text{ cm}^2$$
$$10\,000 \text{ cm}^2 = 1 \text{ m}^2$$
$$10\,000 \text{ m}^2 = 1 \text{ hectare}$$
$$100 \text{ ha} = 1 \text{ km}^2$$

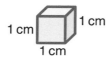

Two football pitches are approximately equal to one hectare.

Volume

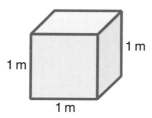

$1 \text{ cm}^3 = 1 \text{ cm} \times 1 \text{ cm} \times 1 \text{ cm} = $ one cubic centimetre

$1 \text{ m}^3 = 1 \text{ m} \times 1 \text{ m} \times 1 \text{ m} = $ one cubic metre

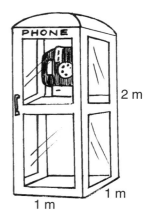

A telephone box is about 2 m³
$2 \text{ m} \times 1 \text{ m} \times 1 \text{ m} = 2 \text{ m}^3$

Capacity

1000 millilitres = 1 litre
1000 litres = 1 kilolitre

Mass

1000 grams = 1 kilogram
1000 kilograms = 1 tonne

Temperature

0° Celsius = melting point of ice
4° C = temperature inside a refrigerator
37° C = human body temperature
100° C = boiling point of water

Time

FACTS	SEASONS	DAYS IN A MONTH
60 seconds = 1 minute 60 minutes = 1 hour 24 hours = 1 day 7 days = 1 week 2 weeks = 1 fortnight 12 months = 1 year 52 weeks = 1 year 365 days = 1 year 366 days = 1 leap year	*Winter* December, January, February *Spring* March, April, May *Summer* June, July, August *Autumn* September, October, November	Thirty days hath September, April, June and November. All the rest have thirty-one Excepting February alone Which hath but twenty-eight days clear And twenty-nine in each leap year.

Telling the time—some examples

ANALOGUE	DIGITAL	24 HOUR
	6:00 a.m.	0600
	9:15 a.m.	0915
	12:00 noon	1200
	3:30 p.m.	1530
	6:00 p.m.	1800
	9:15 p.m.	2115

abacus	An instrument used for calculating. For example, 4 251 =
acute angle	An acute angle is an angle less than 90° which can appear sharp. (Refer to page 31)
add	To put numbers together. For example, 3 + 4 =7
addend	Any number which is added to obtain the sum. For example, 3 + 7 + 8 = 18 　　　　　(**addends**) (sum)
addition	The act of adding (+). (Refer to page 14)
adjacent	Next to. Adjacent sides of a triangle have a common vertex. XY and YZ are adjacent because they have a common vertex, Y.
algorithm	The setting out of a mathematical problem in a certain way. For example,　324　　　874　　　364 　　　　　　　+ 207　　−　23　　×　30
a.m.	ante meridiem (the morning). Any time from midnight to noon.
analogue clock	A clock face with numbers 1 to 12 and two hands.
angle	The amount of turn between two lines around a common point. A figure made of two rays with a common end point.

anti-clockwise	The opposite direction to the normal movement of a clock.
apex	The highest point of a solid (3D) shape from its base.
approximation	To make an estimate of an amount. For example, 398 × 5 can be rounded to 400 × 5 to give an approximation of about 2000.
area	The surface covered by any 2D shape. For example, Area = 6 cm^2 Area can be measured in cm^2, m^2, hectares, km^2. (Refer to p. 44) 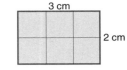
ascending order	To place numbers in increasing order from smallest to largest. For example, 3, 5, 7, 1, 10, 2 becomes 1, 2, 3, 5, 7, 10.
attribute	Any characteristic that can be attributed to a shape when classifying. For example, shapes can be classified according to size, colour, shape, thickness, number of sides.
average (mean)	The total of a series of numbers divided by the amount of numbers in the group. For example, to find the average of 3, 5, 7, 9, add 3 + 5 + 7 + 9 and divide by 4 (number of scores). The average is 6.
axis	A line which divides a shape in half. Example 1. Example 2. The vertical and horizontal axes of a graph. 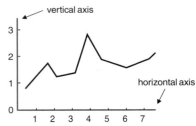
bar chart	(1) A method of recording information. A bar chart is used to show how a total is divided. (Refer to p. 39) 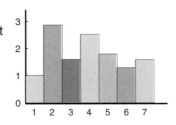 (2) A chart which uses columns to represent data.

base	The bottom face or line of any shape. Example 1. Example 2. base base
base	The number on which a number system is based.
base 10	A decimal number system based on the number 10, our everyday system. (Hindu-Arabic system)
base 10 blocks	Blocks used to display meaning when working in base 10. block flat long short Value 1000 100 10 1 Other values can be assigned to blocks for work in other bases and decimals.
bisect	To divide or cut into two equal sections. Example 1. Bisecting a line Example 2. Bisecting an angle
block graph	A graph made by young children out of blocks to represent data.
breadth	The lesser measurement of a shape which is also called *width*. length breadth
C	The symbol for Celsius and the symbol for century.
calculate	To work out an answer.
capacity	The amount a container can hold. Capacity is also called *volume*. (Refer to p. 46) For example, the capacity of a soft drink can. Capacity can be measured in cm^3, m^3, ml, l, kl. Soft Drink 250 ml

cardinal number	The number of elements in a set. For example, {4, 8, 3, 1, 5} The cardinal number is 5 as the set has 5 elements or members.
carry	See **regroup** p. 72
Celsius	The scale for measuring temperature from 0° to 100°. Some common temperatures are 0°C — the temperature at which ice begins to melt, 100°C — the boiling point of water, 37°C — approximate human body temperature.
census	The entire group. For example, the population of Australia; the number of cars which passed our school between 10 a.m. and 11 a.m.
centicubes	Plastic interlocking cubes with edges measuring one centimetre.
centimetre	One hundredth of 1 metre.

century	One hundred years.
checking	Doing the reverse of an operation to check its correctness. Example

$$\begin{array}{r} 26 \\ +17 \\ \hline 43 \end{array} \qquad \begin{array}{r} 43 \\ -17 \\ \hline 26 \end{array}$$

chord	A line joining two points on the circumference of a circle. (Refer to p. 26)

circle	A plane shape bounded by a continual curved line which is the same distance from its centre point. (Refer to p. 26)

circumference	The distance around a circle. (Refer to pp. 26, 43)

classify	To arrange objects or shapes into groups according to their particular attributes.
	For example, sorting all four-sided shapes from a group of shapes with various numbers of sides.
clockwise	The direction in which the hands of a clock move.
closed curve	A curved line connected to its starting point which encloses an area. (Refer to p. 29)
cm	The abbreviation for centimetre.
complementary	Two angles whose sum adds to make 90°.
	For example, angle A + angle B = 90°.
composite number	A number which results from multiplying two numbers other than itself and one.
	For example, 12 is a composite number because it has factors of 12 × 1, 6 × 2 and 3 × 4.
	Numbers like 7 with only themselves and one as factors are called *prime numbers*.
compute	To work out an answer.
concentric circles	Concentric circles have the same centre. Eccentric circles do not.

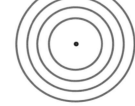

Example 1. concentric circles

Example 2. eccentric circles

congruent	Two shapes that are identical in all ways.

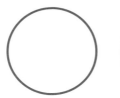   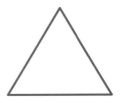

Example 1. congruent circles   Example 2. not congruent triangles

coordinates	Coordinates are used to show position on a grid. The first coordinate refers to the horizontal position (x-axis), the second coordinate refers to the vertical position (y-axis). For example, coordinates (3, 2) Street directories use coordinates.	

cross-section	The face that is left when a solid (3D) shape is cut through.

cube	A three-dimensional shape that has six square faces of equal size. It also has eight vertices and twelve edges. (Refer to p. 32, 34)	

cubic centimetre	A cube used for measuring volume that has sides of one centimetre. (Refer to p. 46, 47, 49) For example, 1 cm sides.	

cubic metre	A cube that has sides of one metre used for measuring volume . (Refer to p. 49)	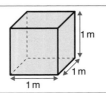

cuboid	A cube-like shape.	

curve	A curved line.

cylinder	A shape which is constructed of two congruent circular faces and one wrap-around rectangular face. A can is a cylinder. (Refer to p. 32)

data	A term used to describe gathered information such as a set of numbers or facts.
day	A 24-hour time period which reflects the time it takes for the earth to complete one revolution.
decade	Ten years.
decagon	A ten-sided shape. (Refer to p. 25)
decahedron	A ten-sided solid shape. (Refer to p. 33)
decimal fraction	Any fraction recorded as a decimal. (Refer to p. 21) For example, 0.1, 0.5, 2.47.
decomposition	A method of subtraction. (Refer to p. 17)
denominator	The bottom number of a fraction that tells how many parts in the whole. (Refer to p. 21)

$$\frac{1}{2} \begin{array}{l} \text{—— numerator} \\ \text{—— } \textbf{denominator} \end{array}$$

descending order	To arrange numbers in decreasing value. For example, 5, 7, 1, 3, 23 would be arranged 23, 7, 5, 3, 1.
diagonal	A line which joins two non-adjacent vertices of a polygon.
diameter	A straight line touching both sides of a circle which passes through the centre point. (Refer to p. 26)

difference	The difference between two numbers (subtraction).
digit	A symbol used in a numeration system to write a numeral. For example, 2 is a 1-digit number, 327 is a 3-digit number.
digital clock	A clock which displays only numerals; it has no hands.
dimension	A measurement of length, breadth or height relating to a line, two-dimensional shape or three-dimensional shape.
direction	The course or line in which anything is directed. For example, up, down, left, right, forward.
displacement	An increase in the level of water in a vessel due to an object being submerged within the vessel, i.e. the volume of the water displaced is equal to its volume. (Refer to p. 48)
dividend	Any amount which is to be divided. For example, $27 \div 3 = 9$ ↑ **dividend**
divisible	A number is divisible if it can be divided without remainders. For example, 12 is divisible by 4, 6, 3, 12, 2 and 1.
division	The mathematical operation that involves breaking up groups or numbers into equal parts. *Sharing* or *grouping* are common terms used when treating division. (Refer to p. 20)
divisor	Any number which is to be divided into the dividend. For example, $27 \div 3 = 9$ ↑ **divisor**
dodecahedron	A solid (3D) shape that has twelve identical faces. (Refer to p. 33)

dot paper	Paper covered with equally-spaced dots and used for graphing or drawing.
double	Twice as much, multiply by two.
dozen	Any group of twelve. For example, 12 eggs.
edge	The intersection of two faces. (Refer to p. 32)
element	An element is a member of a set. For example, "t" is an element of the alphabet.
ellipse	An oval-shaped closed curve.
equal	The same in value or amount. Example 1. Example 2. $3 + 7 = 10$
equal addends	A method of subtraction, sometimes referred to as the *Borrow and Pay Back* method. It is rarely taught in Australian schools. (Refer to p. 18)
equilateral triangle	A triangle that has three equal sides and three equal angles. (Refer to p. 27)
equivalent fractions	Fractions of the same value. $\frac{2}{4} = \frac{1}{2}$
estimate	A rough calculation, not a guess. For example, 307×3 can be viewed as 300×3 to give an estimate of 900.
expanded notation	A means of expanding numbers. For example, $3\ 456 = 3\ 000 + 400 + 50 + 6$ $= (3 \times 1000) + (4 \times 100) + (5 \times 10) + 6$ $= (3 \times 10^3) + (4 \times 10^2) + (5 \times 10) + 6$

exponent	Another term for index. (Refer to p. 8) For example, 10^3 (3 is the exponent) $10^3 = 10 \times 10 \times 10 = 1000$
faces	The surfaces of a three dimensional (solid) shape. (Refer to p. 32)
factor	Any whole number that can be multiplied with another to make a given number. For example, the factors of 12 are 6, 4, 3, 2, 1 and 12. 7 is not a factor of 12 as it cannot be multiplied by another number to give twelve.
factor tree	A diagram that displays factors of a number. (Refer to p. 8)
flip	To turn over a shape.
fraction	Any part of a whole, group, line, etc. (Refer to p. 21)
front view	The frontal view of a 3D object. (Refer to p. 36)
geo-board	A board studded with pegs that elastic bands are placed around to make shapes.

geo-strips	Strips that are joined together to make shapes. They can be used to test rigidity.
gram	A unit for measuring mass. There are 1000 grams in 1 kilogram.
graph	A visual way of recording information. There are many types of graphs — column, bar, line and pie. (Refer to pp. 37, 38)
	A column graph
greater than >	The greater than symbol shows relationships between numbers. It is often used for true and false questions. For example, 27>15
grid paper	Squared paper often used for graphing.
gross	Twelve dozen (144).
gross mass	The total mass of any item including its packaging.
grouping	Breaking things into groups, used in the teaching of division. For example, $12 \div 3 = 4$
ha	The symbol for hectare.
hectare	A hectare is a large measurement of area used for measuring land. A hectare measures 10 000 m².

50 m 1 hectare 100 m

200 m 1 hectare

100 m

Both may be viewed as hectares. (Refer to p. 46)

hemisphere	One half of a sphere.

heptagon	A two-dimensional shape with seven sides.

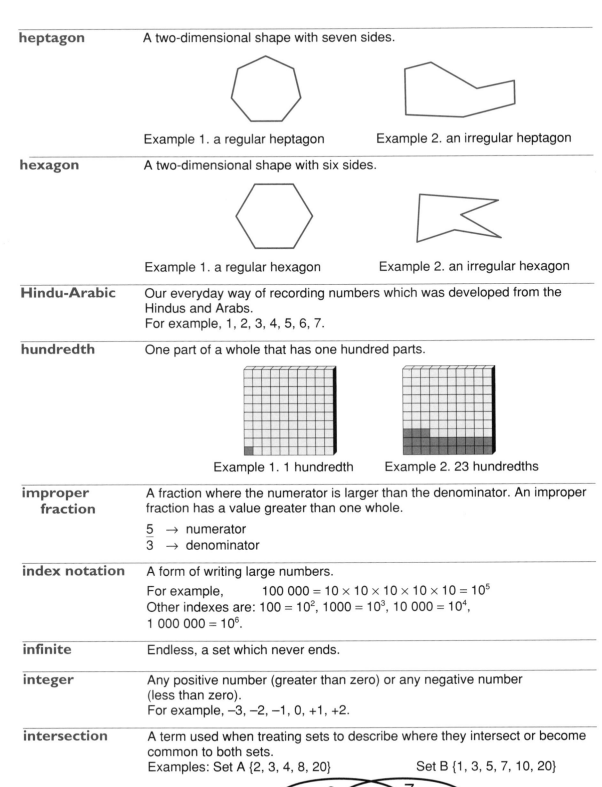

Example 1. a regular heptagon   Example 2. an irregular heptagon

hexagon	A two-dimensional shape with six sides.

Example 1. a regular hexagon   Example 2. an irregular hexagon

Hindu-Arabic	Our everyday way of recording numbers which was developed from the Hindus and Arabs. For example, 1, 2, 3, 4, 5, 6, 7.
hundredth	One part of a whole that has one hundred parts.

Example 1. 1 hundredth   Example 2. 23 hundredths

improper fraction	A fraction where the numerator is larger than the denominator. An improper fraction has a value greater than one whole. $\dfrac{5}{3}$ $\rightarrow$ numerator $\rightarrow$ denominator
index notation	A form of writing large numbers. For example, $100\,000 = 10 \times 10 \times 10 \times 10 \times 10 = 10^5$ Other indexes are: $100 = 10^2$, $1000 = 10^3$, $10\,000 = 10^4$, $1\,000\,000 = 10^6$.
infinite	Endless, a set which never ends.
integer	Any positive number (greater than zero) or any negative number (less than zero). For example, -3, -2, -1, 0, $+1$, $+2$.
intersection	A term used when treating sets to describe where they intersect or become common to both sets. Examples: Set A {2, 3, 4, 8, 20} Set B {1, 3, 5, 7, 10, 20}

The intersection of Set A and Set B is 3, 20.

irregular polygon A polygon which is not in its regular shape.

Example 1. a regular hexagon

Example 2. an irregular hexagon

both have 6 sides

isometric graph/ dot paper Paper used to assist children to do isometric drawings. (Refer to p. 37)

Example 1. graph

Example 2. dot

isosceles triangle A triangle that has two sides and two angles the same. (Refer to p. 27)

kg The symbol for kilogram.

kilolitre A measurement of capacity which is equal to 1000 litres.

kilometre A measurement of length which is equal to 1000 metres.

kl Symbol for kilolitre.

km Symbol for kilometre.

l Symbol for litre.

leap year A leap year happens every four years when there is an extra day added to February. Therefore a leap year has 366 days.

length The longer measurement of any shape or line.
How long something is.

length

width or breadth

less than < The less than symbol shows relationships between numbers. It is often used in true or false questions.
For example, 240 < 420

line (straight)	An undefined term in maths which expresses the idea of a path that does not turn and does not end.
line graph	Information represented on a graph by joining plotted points with a line.

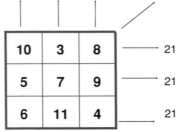

line of symmetry	A line which divides something exactly in half.

litre	A measurement of capacity used to measure liquids. (Refer to p. 49) For example, 1000 millilitres equals 1 litre.

m	Symbol for metre.

magic square	A common number puzzle where all numbers when added either horizontally, vertically or diagonally give the same answer.

Example 1. complete magic square   Example 2. incomplete magic square

mass	The amount of substance in an object. (Refer to p. 49) Common mass measurements are grams, kilograms and tonnes.

mean	Average. (Refer to p. 38)

measure	To work out the length, width, height, mass, volume or area of an object using a standard unit. Examples

 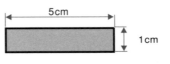

median	The middle score. (Refer to p. 38)
metre	A measurement of length. (Refer to p. 48) 100 centimetres equals 1 metre.
millennium	One thousand years.
millilitre	A measurement of capacity. (Refer to p. 46) 1000 millilitres equals 1 litre. For example, a 1 cm^3 would hold 1 ml of liquid.
millimetre	A measurement of length. There are 10 mm in one centimetre.
minuend	Any number from which another number can be subtracted. $$29 - 7 = 22$$ **minuend**
minus	To take away or subtract, (−).
mirror image	A reflection of an object. (Refer to p. 30)
ml	Symbol for millilitre.
mm	Symbol for millimetre.
mode	The most frequently occurring score. (Refer to p. 38)
multiple	Any number which can be divided equally by another number. For example, 24 is a multiple of 4 because 24 divided by 4 equals 6. Other multiples of 4 are: 4, 8, 12, 16, 20, 24, 28.
multiplicand	The number to be multiplied. For example, $\qquad$ $9 \times 3 = 27$ **multiplicand** $\quad$ multiplier $\quad$ product
multiplication	An operation where a number can be added to itself a number of times. Multiplication can be looked at as repeated addition. (Refer to p. 19) For example, $2 + 2 + 2 + 2 + 2 = 10$ (5 lots of 2) $= 2 \times 5 = 10$
multiplier	The number which multiplies the multiplicand. For example, $\qquad$ $9 \times 3 = 27$ multiplicand $\quad$ **multiplier** $\quad$ product
multiply	The act of multiplication, (×).

negative numbers	Negative numbers have a value less than zero. A minus sign is placed in front of the number to identify it. For example, the lowest temperature in January was −6°C. (Refer to p. 6)

| net | A flat shape which can be folded to make a three-dimensional shape. An unfolded cardboard box is the net of a box. (Refer to p. 34)
For example, the net of a triangular prism |

| net mass | The mass of any object without its packaging. |

| nonagon | A two-dimensional shape with nine sides. |

Example 1.

Example 2.

a regular nonagon

an irregular nonagon

| number | Symbols used to represent quantity.
For example, 1, 2, 45, 657.
Cardinal numbers (Refer to p. 6)
Composite numbers (Refer to p. 6)
Even numbers (Refer to p. 6)
Factor trees (Refer to p. 8)
Index notation (Refer to p. 8)
Odd numbers (Refer to p. 6)
Ordinal numbers (Refer to p. 6)
Prime numbers (Refer to p. 6)
Rational numbers (Refer to p. 6)
Square numbers (Refer to p. 7)
Symbols (Refer to p 5.)
Triangular numbers (Refer to p. 7)
Whole numbers (Refer to p. 6) |

| number line | A line on which numbers are marked. Number lines can be used to represent operations.
For example, $3 + 5 = 8$ |

0 1 2 3 4 5 6 7 8 9 10

| number pattern | Any set of numbers which follows a pattern or a sequence. |

For example,   1, 3, 5, 7, 9, __ , __ . (+ 2)

3, 9, 27, __ , __ . (× 3)

64, 32, 16, 8, __ , __ . (÷ 2)

number sentence	A mathematical sentence written in numerals. For example, $3 + 7 = 10$, $7 \times 3 = 21$
numeral	Any figure or character used to represent a number. For example, 0, 1, 2, 3, 4, 5, 6, 7, 8, 9 etc. Hindu-Arabic numerals (Refer to p. 5) Japanese numerals (Refer to p. 5) Roman numerals (Refer to p. 5)
numerator	The top number of a fraction. (Refer to p. 21) $\underline{2} \rightarrow$ **numerator** $3 \rightarrow$ denominator
obtuse angle	An angle that is larger than 90° but less than 180°. Obtuse angles can appear blunt compared to acute angles, which are less than 90° and appear sharp. (Refer to p. 31)
octahedron	A three-dimensional shape that has eight triangular faces. (Refer to p. 33)
odd number	A number that is not divisible by two. For example, 1, 3, 5, 7, 9, 11, 13
operation	Using addition, multiplication, subtraction, division or a combination of these to solve a mathematical problem. For example, $3 \times 9 = 27$ 3 5 6 − 2 3 4
ordinal number	A number which shows place. For example, 1st, 2nd, 3rd, 4th, 5th, 6th, 7th.
parallel lines	Two or more lines exactly the same distance apart. (Parallel lines need not be the same length.)
parallelogram	A four-sided figure, where each pair of opposite sides are parallel and of equal length.

pattern	A series of shapes, letters, numbers or objects arranged in a recurring series. For example, 4, 14, 24, 34

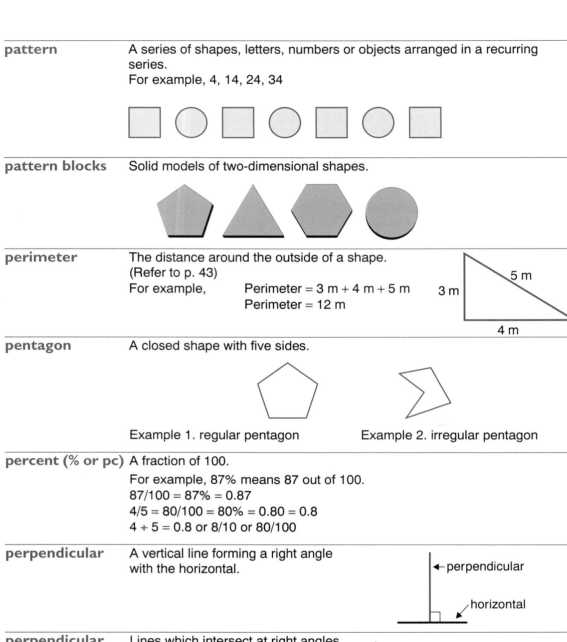

pattern blocks	Solid models of two-dimensional shapes.

perimeter	The distance around the outside of a shape. (Refer to p. 43) For example, Perimeter = 3 m + 4 m + 5 m Perimeter = 12 m

3 m 5 m 4 m

pentagon	A closed shape with five sides.

Example 1. regular pentagon   Example 2. irregular pentagon

percent (% or pc)	A fraction of 100. For example, 87% means 87 out of 100. 87/100 = 87% = 0.87 4/5 = 80/100 = 80% = 0.80 = 0.8 4 ÷ 5 = 0.8 or 8/10 or 80/100

perpendicular	A vertical line forming a right angle with the horizontal.

← perpendicular

horizontal

perpendicular lines	Lines which intersect at right angles.

perspective	Drawing techniques which show similar-sized objects becoming smaller in the distance. (Refer to p. 36)

Pi (π)	The ratio of the circumference of a circle to its diameter.

$$\pi = \frac{\text{circumference}}{\text{diameter}} = 3.14$$

pictogram	A chart using picture symbols to represent quantities.

Pupils visiting library. Each figure represents 5 children.

Mon	👤👤 👤👤 👤👤 👤👤
Tue	👤👤
Wed	👤👤 👤👤 👤👤
Th	👤👤 👤👤
Fri	👤👤 👤👤 👤👤 👤👤 👤👤

pie chart	A circular chart where parts look like portions of a pie.

Also known as *circle sector graphs*.

place value	The value of a digit depending on its place in a numeral. (Refer to p. 13)

For example,

3<u>4</u>6	4 has a value of 40
<u>4</u>95	4 has a value of 400
70<u>4</u>	4 has a value of 4

plan	A diagram focused from above showing the position of objects.

For example, the floor plan of a house (also known as the top view of a 3D object).

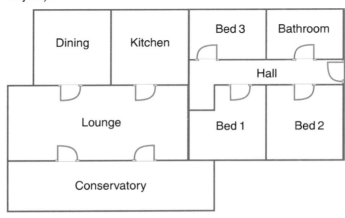

plane	A flat surface, such as a drawing on a page. (Refer to p. 25)

plane shape/ figure	A two-dimensional shape. The boundary of a plane surface. (Refer to p. 25) For example, a square
plus	The symbol for addition, (+) For example, 3 + 2 = 5
p.m.	Abbreviation for the Latin words *post meridiem* which mean *after midday.*
polygon	A closed shape with three or more angles and sides. (Refer to p. 27) For example, triangle, square, rectangle, hexagon, pentagon.
polyhedron	A solid (three-dimensional) shape with plane faces. For example, a cube has six square faces
position	Location of one object in relation to other fixed objects. For example, third from the left; north of Birmingham. (Refer to p. 41)
prime number	A number that is only divisible by itself and 1 (not to be confused with odd numbers). (Refer to p. 6) For example, 2, 3, 5, 7, 11, 13, 17, 19, 23, 29
prism	A solid (three-dimensional) shape which has two bases which are similar and parallel. The sides are parallelograms. (Refer to p. 32)
probability	The likelihood or chance of an event happening. The range of probability extends from zero to one.

0   1

← Unlikely to happen   Likely to happen →

Probability zero: will not happen   Probability one: will happen

Other terms used in everyday language to describe the likelihood of an event happening are: *possibly, probably, likely, unlikely, maybe, might, fifty-fifty, even chance, 99% sure, certain.*

For example, the probability of the referee scoring the winning goal is zero. The probability of *tails* being the result of a coin toss is half (even or fifty-fifty).
The probability of a circle being round is one.

problem	A mathematical problem is a question which requires the application of mathematics in order to provide a solution.

product	The answer achieved after multiplying. For example, $9 \times 3 = 27$ multiplicand multiplier **product**
property	Distinguishing feature common to objects. For example, all triangles have three sides and the total of their angles is 180°.
protractor	An instrument used to measure angles.
pyramid	A solid (three dimensional) shape which has only one base and all other faces are triangular. (Refer to p. 33) For example, a triangular pyramid.
quadrilateral	A plane (two dimensional) shape with four sides. (Refer to p. 28) For example, a square, a rectangle.
quotient	The answer achieved after dividing. $20 \div 4 = 5$ dividend divisor **quotient**
radius	A straight line extending from the centre of a circle to the outside. (Refer to p. 26) (The radius is half the diameter.) radius
random selection	A sample taken in which all items have an equal chance of being selected. No restrictions apply. For example, drawing names out of a hat.
range	The distribution of scores from the lowest frequency to the highest frequency. (Refer to p. 38)
ratio	The number of times one quantity contains another quantity. For example, the ratio of water to fertiliser is 9:1. This means the mixture contains nine times as much water as fertiliser. A ratio of 6:3 means there is twice the quantity of one substance as compared to the other because $6 \div 3 = 2$.
rational number	Any positive or negative whole number or fraction including zero. (Refer to p. 6) For example, -14, -8, -1, 0, $\frac{8}{10}$, 6
rectangle (oblong)	A four-sided figure with four right angles and two pairs of parallel sides. An oblong is a rectangle with two sets of parallel sides of different lengths. A square is also a rectangle.

rectangular prism	A solid (three-dimensional) shape which consists of six rectangular faces. (Refer to p. 32)

reflex angle	An angle between 180° and 360°.

325°

regroup	To alter the formation of a group, usually for a specific purpose.

For example, 34 may be regrouped to 20 and 14. (Refer to p. 17)

i.e.
$$\begin{array}{r} {}^{2}\,{}^{14} \\ \not{3}\,4 \\ -1\,6 \end{array}$$

regular polygon	A plane (two-dimensional) shape which has sides of equal length and equal angles.

triangle   square   pentagon   hexagon

regular polyhedron	A polyhedron with all sides being congruent. For example, a tetrahedron (four equilateral triangles).

remainder	The amount remaining after a number has been divided.

For example, $27 \div 6 = 4$ remainder 3

The remainder may be expressed as a fraction of the divisor, i.e. $27 \div 6 = 4\frac{3}{6}$

revolution	A complete turn of 360°.

○ start

rhombus	A four-sided shape with four equal sides. Opposite angles are equal.

right angle	An angle of 90°.	

---

rigid

A construction which is secure and cannot be altered.

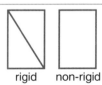

rigid   non-rigid

Roman numerals Number system devised by the Ancient Romans.

1 = I	90 = XC	1000 = M
5 = V	100 = C	1999 = MCMXCIX
9 = IX	400 = CD	2000 = MM
10 = X	500 = D	2001 = MMI
50 = L	900 = CM	

---

rotation

To turn an object about a fixed point. (Shapes are turned to see if they have rotational symmetry.)

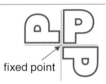

fixed point

---

rounding off

To alter the exact value of a number by giving that number a more convenient value, usually for the purpose of estimating.

For example,   £9 → £10   (nearest 10)
              87p → £1.00 (nearest 100)
              488 → 500   (nearest 100)

NB 5 is always valued upwards.

For example,   4.5 → 5   (nearest whole number)
              45 → 50   (nearest 10)
              105 → 110   (nearest 10)
              105 → 100   (nearest 100)

---

rule

An instruction or pattern to be followed.

For example, rule: multiply by 3

0		2	3	4	5
0	3	6	9		

---

sample

A small percentage of objects taken from the group.

For example, a sample of the children's work was displayed.

scale	A measuring system. temperature mass length time
scale	A ratio which defines the proportion to which a drawing has been altered in comparison with the original. For example, scale 1cm = 10 metres
scalene triangle	A triangle with sides of different lengths and angles of different size. (Refer to p. 27)
scales	Instruments used to measure mass. For example, kitchen scales, bathroom scales.
sector	Part of a circle, bounded by two radii and the arc of the circle.
segment	A part of a line or shape. Example 1. segment of a line Example 2. segment of a circle
semi-circle	Half a circle.
sequence	An order of numbers or objects arranged according to a rule. For example, 5, 10, 15, 20
set	A group of elements belonging to a distinct group. For example, 5 is a member of the set of prime numbers. {1, 3, 5, 7 ,11, ...} is a member of the set of plane shapes.
set square	A triangular instrument used in drawing. 30° 45° 45° 60°

shape	The outline of an object.

Two-dimensional shapes may be classified according to the number of sides they have.
For example, circle, triangle, octagon, pentagon.

Three-dimensional shapes may be classified according to the edges, vertices and surfaces they have.
For example, a triangular prism.

Shapes may be regular or irregular.

regular   irregular |
| **side** | A boundary line of a two-dimensional shape.
For example, a parallelogram has four sides |
| **side view** | The shape an object has when viewed from the side. |
| **signs** | Symbols; abstract representations of a concept or a process. (Refer to p. 4)

For example, $+$ $-$ $\times$ $\div$ $=$ |
| **skeleton (skeletal model)** | The framework of a three-dimensional shape.
For example, the skeleton of a rectangular prism. |
| **slide** | To move a shape in any direction. |
| **solid** | Term used to describe three-dimensional shapes.
(Refer to p. 32) |

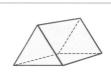

sort	To separate objects according to criteria.
space	The region in which an object exists.
sphere	A perfectly round, three-dimensional shape. For example, a ball.
square	A two-dimensional shape consisting of four equal sides and four right angles. A square is also a rectangle.
square centimetre (cm²)	A unit for measuring area. (Refer to p. 49) For example, 1 cm × 1 cm = 1 cm² 1 cm / 1 cm
square kilometre (km²)	A unit for measuring area. (Refer to p. 49) For example, 1 km × 1 km = 1 km² 1 km / 1 km
square metre (m²)	A unit for measuring area. (Refer to p. 49) For example, 1 m × 1 m = 1 m² 1 m / 1 m
square number	The product of a number multiplied by itself. (Refer to p. 7) For example, $2^2 = 2 \times 2 = 4$ $3^2 = 3 \times 3 = 9$ $4^2 = 4 \times 4 = 16$ $5^2 = 5 \times 5 = 25$ Any number that can be represented in the shape of a square.
square paper	Paper with a square grid pattern. Used when constructing two-dimensional drawings and graphs.
statistics	The collection, organisation and presentation of data. (Refer to p. 38)
straight angle	It is an angle of 180° made up of two right angles. (Refer to p. 31) 90° 90°

subtract	To remove part of a group. To find the difference in value. (Refer to pp. 15–18)
subtrahend	The number being subtracted. (Refer to p. 16) For example,　　　9 − 5 = 4 　　　　minuend　**subtrahend**　difference
sum	The total after addition.
supplementary angles	Two angles which have a total of 180°. For example, 130° + 50° = 180° 130°　50°
surface	The outer face or outside of an object. A surface may be flat or curved.
surface area	The total area of all faces of a three-dimensional object. For example, the net of a rectangular prism showing its six surfaces. (Refer to p. 44)
symmetry	A shape has line symmetry if both its parts match when it is folded along a line.
tables	Lists of multiplication facts. (Refer to p. 11) For example,　　0 × 3 = 0　　1 × 3 = 3　　2 × 3 = 6　　3 × 3 = 9
take away	To subtract. (Refer to p. 15) For example, eight take away three equals five, or 8 − 3 = 5.
tally	To keep count by placing a stroke to represent each item. The fifth stroke usually crosses the four preceding strokes. (Refer to p. 37) For example,　卌 卌 卌 卌 II = 22
tangram	A square cut into seven pieces. Traditional Chinese tangrams are arranged to make pictures.
temperature	A measure of the hotness or coldness of an object. Temperature is measured in degrees Celsius. For example,　　　　0°C　the melting point of ice 　　　　100°C　the boiling point of water

tessellation	A tessellation is formed by the repetition of one or more shapes so that they fit together without leaving gaps or overlapping. Tiles and bricks are laid in a tessellating pattern. (Refer to p. 29) For example, a honeycomb pattern using regular hexagons. 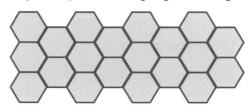
tetrahedron	A triangular pyramid. (Refer to p. 33)
thermometer	An instrument used to measure temperature.
three-dimensional (3D)	Solid objects have three dimensions: height, length and width. (Refer to p. 32) 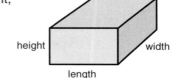
time line	A line which represents a span of time. Periods of time within that span can be shown by intervals. 
tonne (t)	1000 kilograms (Refer to p. 49)
top view	The shape an object has when viewed from above. (Refer to p. 36) 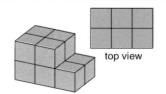
total	The result of addition. For example, the total = 30p + +
trapezium	A four-sided figure with only one pair of parallel sides. 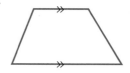

triangle	A two-dimensional shape with three sides and three angles. The sum of the angles is 180°. (Refer to p. 27)

trundle wheel	A wheel with a circumference of 1 metre. It is designed to click at the completion of one rotation, enabling the operator to record the number of clicks (metres). It can be used to measure distances such as the perimeter of the school playground.

turn	To rotate a shape around a point.

twelve hour time	Traditional clocks and watches show time divided into 12 hours. (Refer to p. 50)
	For example, 20 to 11 or 10:40

twenty-four hour time	Some digital clocks and watches display time divided into 24 hour intervals, so as to distinguish between a.m. and p.m. (Refer to p. 50)
	Example 1. 8 minutes to 2 or 1:52 p.m. or 13:52
	Example 2. The video recorder was set for the news at 18:00.

two-dimensional (2D)	Plane shapes have only two dimensions such as length and width. (Refer to p. 25)

unit	A unit is one. The units column is the ones column.

H	T	U
4	5	6

```
   400
    50
 +  6
  456
```

units (basic)	Formal units are used for specific measurements. (Refer to pp. 48–50)
	For example, length → metre
	mass → kilogram
	temperature → degrees Celsius
	time → second

vertex	The point where two or more lines meet to form an angle.

vertical	Upright; a straight line at right angles to the horizontal.

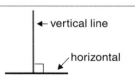

vertices	Plural of vertex. For example, a triangle has 3 vertices.

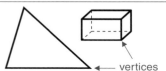

volume	The volume of a substance is the amount of space it occupies. The basic units for recording volume are the cubic metre (m³), the cubic centimetre (cm³), the litre (l) and millilitre (ml). (Refer to p. 46)

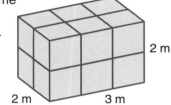

The volume of three-dimensional objects can be determined by applying this formula:

Volume = length × width × height

The volume of this rectangular prism is 12 m³,

i.e.   2 m × 3 m × 2 m = 12 m³

weight	In everyday use, the terms *weight* and *mass* are interchangeable. In mathematics, mass is the amount of matter in an object. The weight of an object alters according to the height above sea level. For example, an astronaut experiences weightlessness in space.

whole numbers	The counting numbers from zero to infinity. (Refer to p. 6) 0, 1, 2, 3, 4, →

width	The distance from side to side on the shorter side.

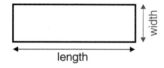

zero	The numeral 0. Other terms are *nought, nothing, nil* and *none.*